THIS WALKER BOOK BELONGS TO:

_____

_____

_____

_____

For Charlie
E.B.

For my sisters
E.H.

First published 1976 by Ernest Benn Ltd
This edition published 1992 by
Walker Books Ltd, 87 Vauxhall Walk
London SE11 5HJ

Text © 1976 Elisabeth Beresford
Illustrations © 1992 Edgar Hodges
Illustrations based on original film puppets
designed by Ivor Wood © 1972 FilmFair

Printed and bound in Hong Kong by
Imago Publishing Ltd

British Library Cataloguing in Publication Data
Beresford, Elisabeth
The MacWomble's pipe band.
I. Title   II. Hodges, Edgar
823'.914 [J]   PZ7
ISBN 0-7445-1772-9
ISBN 0-7445-2152-1 (Pbk)

THE
MACWOMBLE'S
PIPE BAND

Written by
ELISABETH BERESFORD
Illustrations by EDGAR HODGES
based on the original film puppets
designed by Ivor Wood

WALKER BOOKS
LONDON

Cairngorm The MacWomble The Terrible (to give him his full name) had come down from his home in Scotland to stay with his Womble cousins in their Wimbledon burrow. He hadn't chosen a very good time for his visit as the weather was cold, wet and windy.

"It reminds me of the Highlands, so it does," said The MacWomble.

"Yes," said Great Uncle Bulgaria. "And I haven't seen a single Human Being on the Common today. But they are a silly lot. They seem to think a spot of rain will make them melt. And that means," he went on rather grumpily, "that there'll be little or no rubbish for the young Wombles to tidy up."

"And mischief finds work for idle paws," said The MacWomble, quoting an old Womble proverb. "They'll be up to all kinds of tricks. If I was in charge of this burrow I would…"

"Well you're not!" snapped Great Uncle Bulgaria. "I am. I shall go to my study and think of an answer to the problem. Excuse me, MacWomble."

The MacWomble's little round eyes twinkled, but he didn't say anything. He knew perfectly well that after the very good lunch Madame Cholet had given them, Great Uncle Bulgaria would soon be having a nice little nap. And as The MacWomble loved to be in charge, he decided that he would see what he could do, so off he strode with his kilt swinging to the Library.

Wellington was sitting with his paws over his ears. He was trying to keep out the noise his friends were making as they played Blind Womble's Buff all over the burrow at the tops of their voices.

Spread in front of Wellington was a very large magazine full of coloured pictures.

"What have you there, young Wellington?" asked The MacWomble.

"Oh! What? Sorry!" said Wellington. "It's you, MacWomble. Sorry. I say, isn't this a smashing magazine, Just look at..."

"It'll be English, no doubt," said The MacWomble, not sounding at all interested.

"Oh no, it's – er – Scotch."

"*Scottish*!" The MacWomble corrected him. "Well, let me have a look. It's bound to be a grand wee paper in that case. Och will you look at that then, a picture of a massed pipe band. It almost makes me feel homesick. Oh for the sound and the skirl of the pipes, oh for the, the..."

And he stopped dead.

"Sorry, but oh for the what?" asked
Wellington, after several seconds of silence.

"That's it!" said The MacWomble. "We'll
form the Wimbledon Massed Pipe Band.
We'll make our own bagpipes and I'll teach
you all how to play them."

"Call all the other young Wombles and tell them to report to me in the Workshop *immediately*. Don't just sit there with your wee eyes popping, there's wuuuurk to be done."

As everyone else had got very bored just playing games, they all arrived in the Workshop in double quick time, and there they found The MacWomble talking to Tobermory.

"You want to do WHAT?" asked Tobermory.

"Och, Womble, how many times do I have to tell you, we want some pieces of wee rubbish which we can make into grand, great SCOTTISH bagpipes," replied The MacWomble thumping his paw on the work table.

"Well, I dunno, I'm sure," said Tobermory. "Does Great Uncle Bulgaria know about this plan?"

"No, no, it'll be a grand surprise for him."

"I'll bet it will," said Tobermory. "Well, you'd better try the little storeroom third on the left. It's full of bits of piping and old plastic bags and that. But once you've made your bagpipes don't you start playing them in there. The noise – ahem – I mean the music'd put me off my work."

"We'll trouble you no further," said The MacWomble in a very grand manner. "Band, forward march. Left, right, left, right…" Tobermory watched them out of sight and then tapped the barometer. The needle stayed firmly at "wild and stormy" and Tobermory shook his head, went "tck, tck, tck" and returned to his job of making new shelves for the kitchen.

The MacWomble was as good as his word…

For the rest of the day he and the young Wombles shut themselves in the storeroom and worked very, very hard. A great deal of sawing and hammering and sometimes cries of "ouch, that was my paw, Bungo" and "look out, Orinoco, you nearly put that pipe in my eye", were heard faintly in the background, but apart from that, the burrow was strangely peaceful…

The next morning, the Wimbledon Pipe
Band marched out on to the deserted wet and
windy Common. It wasn't really a very big
band as it had only six players, Orinoco,
Tomsk, Wellington, Bungo, Alderney and
Shansi, her best friend. As Shansi is very neat
with her paws and is always top in Womble
paw-craft lessons, it wasn't surprising that
she was the best at playing the bagpipes.

"Yon's a grand wee Womble," said The MacWomble, who was enjoying himself enormously. "Play the opening bars again." The wailing sound which Shansi produced from her home-made bagpipes was so unusual that every squirrel, hedgehog, mouse and bird ran for their lives.

"Grand," said The MacWomble. "Now the rest of you try it. One, two, three – play!"

Everybody else was enjoying themselves too, as they puffed and blew and stamped their paws, for it's enormous fun making your own music.

"Grand, grand," said The MacWomble at the end of the fourth day of band practice. "Tomorrow we'll give our first concert. It'll be a great surprise for Great Uncle Bulgaria."

It was! Great Uncle Bulgaria, Madame Cholet, Tobermory and the very small Wombles from the Womblegarten were all very surprised indeed.

"You do realize, Madame Cholet," murmured Great Uncle Bulgaria, looking at his programme, "that this is only the *first* concert? And that there are another FOUR to come?"

"*Tiens, alors,*" said Madame Cholet.

"Tck, tck, tck," said Tobermory, and he went over to the barometer and tapped it. Then they all went out on to the Common to wait for the concert. A wailing sound grew louder and LOUDER and LOUDER until the pipe band came to a halt in front of Great Uncle Bulgaria.

"And now," said The MacWomble, "a special tune which I myself have composed. It's called *For you'll take the large rubbish and I'll take the small rubbish but I'll have a full tidy-bag afore ye*. Band, one, two, three, MARCH!"

During the next ten minutes, the Wimbledon Pipe Band played for all they were worth. Their home-made bagpipes squeaked and groaned and wailed and hooted, and they were completely unaware that their audience was not enjoying the concert quite as much as they were. However, as Wombles are the most polite creatures in the world, everybody clapped at the finish.

"Thank you, thank you," said The MacWomble. "Now tomorrow night we shall play you a Wimbledon Highland Jig, followed by..."

"Tck, tck, tck," said Tobermory. "What a very good idea, but I'm afraid, MacWomble, that by then it won't be possible. You see the weather is changing. It has already stopped raining and by tomorrow it will probably be warm, bright and sunny."

"Dear me," said Great Uncle Bulgaria. "What a relief. Ahem. What I mean is, what a great relief it will be for all those Human Beings who will start walking across the Common and, no doubt, begin to drop litter in their usual untidy way. Which in turn means all you young Wombles will have a great deal of work to do. How sad it is to think that you won't have the time or the energy to give us another little concert. Thank you so much, MacWomble, for this evening's entertainment, and thank you to the Wimbledon Pipe Band."

The Band looked at each other a little bit sadly and then at The MacWomble, who drew himself up, shook his head and then said, "Just when I was getting my pipers into shape too. Well, it can't be helped, I suppose. Pipers," and he turned towards his band, "we'll play the lament I taught you, all the way back to the burrow. Are you ready? One, two, three – March!" And the first – and last – Wimbledon Pipe Band, with The MacWomble at their head, played their way – really quite well too – back to the Wimbledon burrow.

MORE WALKER PAPERBACKS
For You to Enjoy

THE WOMBLES OF WIMBLEDON
by Elisabeth Beresford/Edgar Hodges

ORINOCO RUNS AWAY
Orinoco gets into trouble when he dips his paws into
Madame Cholet's cake mixture!
ISBN 0-7445-2127-0   £2.99

THE SNOW WOMBLE
One morning, the Wombles wake up to find their common covered in snow.
Orinoco thinks it's ice-cream and tries to eat it. Tomsk takes a
tray and goes tobogganing.
Bungo, meanwhile, builds a very familiar-looking snow Womble!
ISBN 0-7445-2128-9   £2.99

WELLINGTON AND THE BLUE BALLOON
Great Uncle Bulgaria offers a prize of two helpings of dinner to the first Womble
to return to the burrow with a full tidy bag. The race is on, but Wellington
doesn't think he stands a chance of winning – until he finds a blue balloon,
which makes him look at things in a completely different way!
ISBN 0-7445-2154-8   £2.99

Walker Paperbacks are available from most booksellers, or by post from
Walker Books Ltd, PO Box 11, Falmouth, Cornwall TR10 9EN.

To order, send: title, author, ISBN number and price for each book ordered, your full name and address
and a cheque or postal order for the total amount, plus postage and packing:

UK and BFPO Customers – £1.00 for first book, plus 50p for the second book and plus 30p for each additional book to a maximum charge of £3.00.
Overseas and Eire Customers – £2.00 for first book, plus £1.00 for the second book and plus 50p per copy for each additional book.
Prices are correct at time of going to press, but are subject to change without notice.